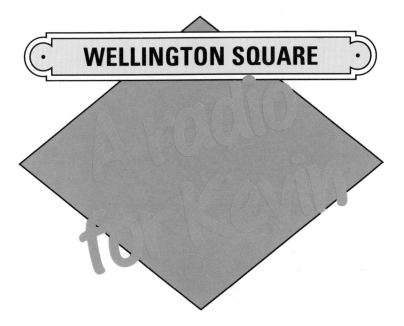

# WELLINGTON SQUARE

## A radio for Kevin

**KEITH GAINES**

ILLUSTRATED BY
**JON DAVIS**

Nelson

Kevin was mad about music.
He always listened to music on the radio.
But now he did not have a radio.

His old radio had broken.
Kevin had put his broken radio in a box,
but then he had left his box on a bench in the park.
Someone had found the box with wires sticking
out of it.

Someone had thought it was a bomb.
Someone had thought it was going to blow up.
Someone had called the police.
A man who knew about bombs
came and looked at the box.
He had not been sure if the box was a bomb or not.

The man had blown up the radio.
After a bright flash and a loud bang,
there was not much left of the radio.

Kevin still did not know who had called the police, or who had told them it was a bomb.

Now Kevin had no radio.
'How can I get a radio?' thought Kevin.
'Let's see how much money I have.'

Kevin did not have much money.
'I could not buy a radio with that,' he thought.
'I could just about buy a bag of chips.
I will see my Dad about a radio.'

'Can I have a radio?' he asked his Dad.

'Yes, Kevin,' said Mr Miller.

'You can have a radio for your next birthday.'

'But I have only just had a birthday,' said Kevin.
'I want a radio before my next birthday.'

10

His Dad looked at Kevin.
'If you want one before your next birthday,
then I'm afraid you will have to buy your own radio.'
'But I have no money,' said Kevin.

'Then you will have to think of a way of
getting some money,' said Mr Miller.

'What do you like doing?' said Mr Miller.
'I like eating,' said Kevin.
'I don't think people would pay good
money just to see you eat,' said his Dad.

Just then, a lady came up to Mr Miller.
'Can you have a look at my car, please?'
said the lady.
'It's making a strange noise.
It's a sort of ticking sound.'
Mr Miller went to look at the car.

Mr Miller looked in the car.
'I'm afraid it's not very clean,' said the lady.
'It's quite a mess.
At home, I have to park it under a tree.'

'This is what's making the ticking sound,'
said Mr Miller.
'I will get you another one.
It won't take very long to put in.'

16

Kevin went up to the lady.
'Would you like me to clean your car?' said Kevin.
'Yes, please,' said the lady.

When Mr Miller came back,
Kevin was cleaning the car.

The lady gave Mr Miller the money for
mending the car.
Then she looked at her car.
The car shone.
'It's lovely and clean now,' said the lady.
'Here is something for you.'
The lady gave Kevin some money for
cleaning the car.

'Do you always clean cars here?'
asked the lady as she was opening the door.
'No, we don't,' said Mr Miller.
'Yes, we do,' said Kevin quickly.
'But only after school.'
'I will tell my friends about you,' said the lady.

20

'Why did you tell her we do car cleaning?'
asked Mr Miller.
'If I clean cars after school,
I will get the money to buy a radio,' said Kevin.
'I like cars and I like cleaning them.'

The next day, after school, Kevin put up a poster.
The poster was to tell people about the car cleaning.
Soon, Kevin was cleaning two or three cars a day.

Kevin bought a radio.
It was a good radio.
It was very loud.

After Kevin had bought his radio,
he still went on cleaning cars.
But now he listened to music too!